The Fox and the Stork

and other Aesop's Fables

Compiled by Vic Parker

Miles Kelly

First published in 2013 by Miles Kelly Publishing Ltd

Harding's Barn, Bardfield End Green, Thaxted, Essex, CM6 3PX, UK

2 4 6 8 10 9 7 5 3 1

Publishing Director Belinda Gallagher
Creative Director Jo Cowan
Editorial Director Rosie McGuire
Designer Joe Jones
Production Manager Elizabeth Collins
Reprographics Stephan Davis, Jennifer Hunt, Thom Allaway

ISBN 978-1-84810-936-0

Printed in China

British Library Cataloguing-in-Publication Data
A catalogue record for this book is available from the British Library

ACKNOWLEDGMENTS
The publishers would like to thank the following artists who have contributed to this book:
Cover: Natalie Hinrichsen at Advocate Art
Advocate Art: Natalie Hinrichsen, Tamsin Hinrichsen
The Bright Agency: Marcin Piwowarski
Frank Endersby
Marco Furlotti
Jan Lewis (decorative frames)

Made with paper from a sustainable forest

www.mileskelly.net   info@mileskelly.net

www.factsforprojects.com

Contents

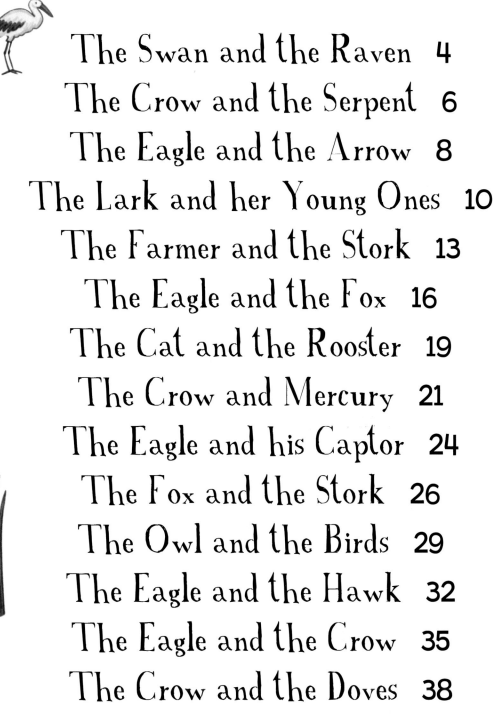

The Swan
and the
Raven

A raven once caught sight of a swan and couldn't help but feel jealous at the elegant bird's long neck and snow-white feathers. The raven became eaten up with envy. All he could think of was how he too could get the same beautiful plumage.

'Maybe the swan's clean color comes from the water in which he swims?' the raven wondered. So he went to soak himself in the swan's lakes and pools. But no matter how many times the raven washed, he didn't

become even a tiny bit white. Instead, he was tired and hungry, as he couldn't find any food. In the end, he returned to his old habitat and had to be satisfied with his lot.

You can try to change your behavior but it won't change what you are.

The Crow and the Serpent

There was once a crow who was starving. He used what little energy he had left to set out on one last flight to find food. Imagine how relieved he was when he noticed a serpent asleep in a sunny nook. Swooping down, the crow seized it greedily.

The serpent was not about to die without a fight. It suddenly darted forward, biting the crow with a mortal wound.

The crow died in agony from the poison, saying, "Oh unhappy me!

6

I thought I had got lucky but in fact I had discovered my own downfall!"

What seems to be a blessing is not always the case.

The Eagle and the Arrow

O nce upon a time, a mighty eagle was soaring through the air, strong and powerful. Suddenly it heard the whizz of a speeding arrow, and felt itself pierced in the heart.

The eagle looked down and saw that it was indeed badly wounded, with blood pouring from its breast. Slowly the bird fluttered down to the ground, where it lay dying.

Looking down upon the arrow with which it

had been pierced, the eagle's last thought was the realization that the shaft of the arrow had been decorated with one of its own feathers.

We often give our enemies the means for our own destruction.

The Lark
and her
Young Ones

Long ago, in early springtime one year, a lark made her nest in the green stalks of some very young wheat. She laid a clutch of tiny eggs and looked after them carefully until they hatched. Then she cared for her brood with the utmost attention until they had almost grown to their full strength. The lark's little ones had grown nearly all their wing feathers, and were almost able to fly, when the owner of the field came to look over his crop – which by now was fully grown and ripe.

"The wheat is ready," he said to himself. "The time has come when I must ask my neighbors to help me with this year's harvest."

One of the young larks heard his words and anxiously hurried to tell his mother. "We can't stay here, Mother," he warned, "it isn't safe. Wherever shall we go?"

"Don't worry, my son," his mother urged. "There is no reason to move quite yet. The man is only going to ask his friends to help him with the harvest, he's not going to do anything straight away."

It was indeed a few days later before the owner of the field came again. By this time, the

grain was falling from the wheat because it was becoming over-ripe. "Hmm..." he said. "I really must come myself tomorrow with my men, and with as many other reapers as I can hire, and I will get in the harvest."

The mother lark heard these words herself and said to her brood, "It is time to be off now, my little ones, for the man is in earnest this time – he no longer trusts his friends, but will reap the field himself."

Depend on yourself more than others.

The Farmer and the Stork

O ne spring, a farmer and his workers toiled away to plow the fields and sow the seed, doing their best to ensure a good harvest later in the year. However, no sooner was all the seed in the ground than a flock of cranes swooped down and began to peck at it.

The farmer and his men tried everything they could think of to get rid of the cranes – from running at the birds while flapping their arms, to setting up scarecrows – but the cranes kept coming back. In the end, the

farmer decided to lay nets all over the fields, which would not keep the birds away, but might catch them when they landed.

Sure enough, when the farmer went out to check his fields the next day there was a stork trapped in one of the nets. It was flapping its wings frantically, trying to get free.

"Please spare my life," the stork begged. "I ask you to let me go free this once. I think my leg is broken – please have pity on me. Besides, I know you set these nets to catch cranes. I am not a crane, I am a stork, a bird of excellent character. Look at my feathers – they are not at all like a crane's."

However, the farmer just laughed and said, "It may be all as you

say, but I only know this: I have caught you in the company of those robbers the cranes, and you must die in their company too."

Birds of a feather flock together.

The Eagle
and the
Fox

Long ago, there lived an eagle and a fox who struck up a friendship and decided to live near each other. The eagle built her nest in a tall tree, and hatched a brood of chicks, while the fox crept into the undergrowth and produced her young there.

Not long after they had agreed upon this plan, the eagle failed to find any food for her chicks for

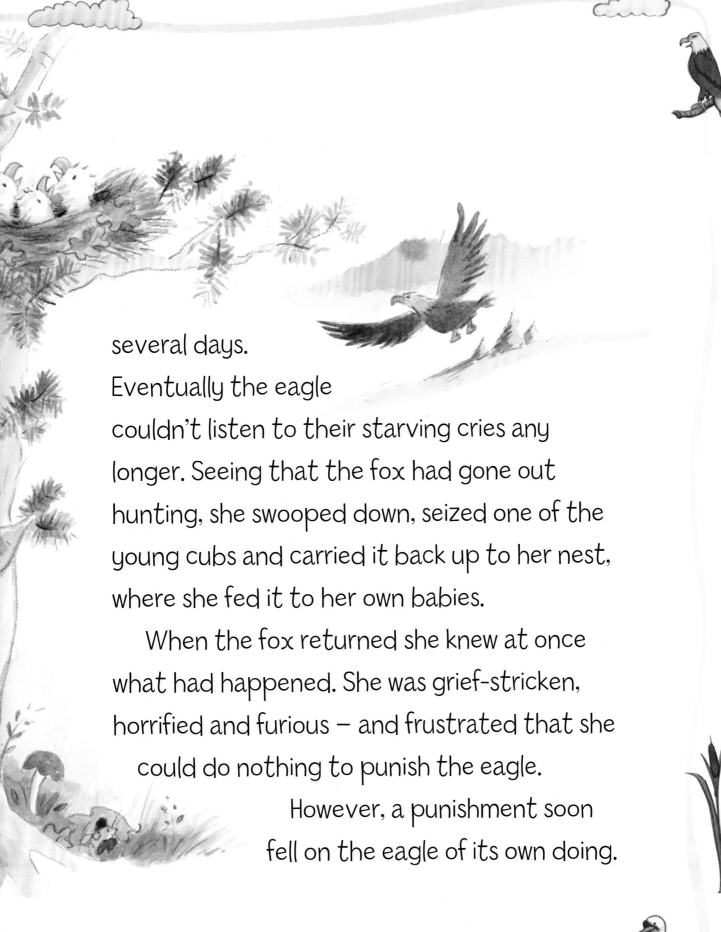

several days.
Eventually the eagle
couldn't listen to their starving cries any
longer. Seeing that the fox had gone out
hunting, she swooped down, seized one of the
young cubs and carried it back up to her nest,
where she fed it to her own babies.

When the fox returned she knew at once
what had happened. She was grief-stricken,
horrified and furious – and frustrated that she
could do nothing to punish the eagle.

However, a punishment soon
fell on the eagle of its own doing.

Not long afterwards, the eagle was hovering near a fire on which some villagers were cooking a goat, when she seized a piece of the flesh, and carried it to her nest. She did not realize that a burning cinder was attached to the piece of meat. A strong breeze soon fanned the spark into a flame, and the eaglets, as yet with no wing feathers and therefore totally helpless, were roasted in their nest. The dead eaglets dropped at the foot of the tree, where the fox and her young made a tasty meal of them.

What goes around comes around.

The Cat and the Rooster

A cat was slinking about in the fields one day when he caught a special treat – a rooster. The cat began to think how he could justify killing and

eating the rooster.

"People would thank me for getting rid of you," he yowled, "because you crow at night and keep everyone awake."

"But Mr Cat, that's not true – people think I'm useful," the rooster blustered, "for I do it to help everyone get up in time to go to work."

Then the cat gave a shrug and said, "Well, no matter. Whatever you say, I'm not going to go without supper." And he made a meal of him.

A villain doesn't need a reason for carrying out a crime.

The Crow and Mercury

A long time ago, a crow became caught in a trap. He prayed to the great god Apollo to release him, and he vowed that if the god did indeed help him, he would pray and make a special offering at the god's shrine.

Apollo heard the creature's desperate cries and came to his rescue – the crow suddenly found that the trap snapped open, releasing his leg. The crow was overjoyed.

However, the minute he hopped away and took to the skies, he totally forgot his promise.

He went nowhere near Apollo's shrine but hurried straight back to his family and friends. Shortly afterwards, the crow again became caught in a trap. He didn't dare to ask Apollo for help once more, so instead he

offered up the same promise to the god Mercury. But the crow was not so lucky a second time. Mercury suddenly appeared before

him and said, "Do you take me for a fool? How can I believe your vows, when you have clearly lied to my friend?"

Always keep your promises.

The Eagle
and his
Captor

A mighty eagle was once captured by a man, who immediately clipped its wings so it could no longer fly. As if this wasn't enough humiliation, the man then put the eagle – Lord of the Birds – into his poultry yard with all the common chickens, turkeys and geese. Of course, at this, the eagle was weighed down with grief.

Some time later, another man bought the eagle for a large sum of money. This man allowed the eagle's feathers to grow again and then set it free.

The eagle couldn't believe the man's kindness. Overjoyed to be flying, it soared into the skies. Then it swooped back down and caught a hare, taking it to the man as a gift.

A passing fox saw what the eagle had done and couldn't believe it. "What are you doing trying to please this man?" he exclaimed. "You should be trying to win the kindness of your former owner. You never know, he may hunt for you again and clip your wings a second time."

Keep your friends close but your enemies closer.

The Fox and the Stork

There was once a time when a fox and a stork were good friends. They enjoyed each other's company, chatting about this and that, and often went to visit each other.

Once, the fox invited the stork to dinner. He thought he would play a joke on her. So when it came to serving the meal, he put nothing in front of her except some soup in a very shallow dish. There was nothing else to eat, and no spoon either. The fox could easily lap up his soup with his tongue. But of course the stork had a

very long, thin bill, which was no good for lapping up soup. All she could do was dip the end of her bill in the shallow dish. She was very disappointed and left the meal as hungry as when she arrived.

The fox laughed to himself when he saw that the stork had to leave her soup. "I'm sorry," he said, "that the soup is not to your liking."

"Do not apologize," said the stork as she left. "I've had a lovely time and I hope you will come to me for dinner soon." So they fixed a date when the fox would go for dinner at the stork's house.

When the day came, and the pair were seated at the table in the stork's kitchen, the fox saw that the meal was contained in a very long, narrow jar. Even though the fox had quite a long, thin nose, the jar was even longer and thinner. He couldn't reach any of the delicious soup inside. All he could manage to do was to lick

the top of the jar. However, the stork could easily fit her long, thin bill inside.

"I will not apologize," said the stork "because you should do as you would be done by."

Treat others as you would wish to be treated.

The Owl and the Birds

There was once an owl, who, in her wisdom, advised the rest of the birds that whenever they noticed a little shoot growing from an acorn, they should pull it up out of the ground. The owl said that acorns encouraged the growth of mistletoe, from which hunters could make sticky bird-lime. The hunters would then paste the bird-lime onto reeds, which they would place in trees, bushes and hedgerows. Then birds would get stuck to the reeds and be caught by the hunters.

The owl also advised the other birds to pluck up the seed of the flax plant, which people often grew as crops. The flax was then used to make nets and snares to trap birds.

Lastly the owl, seeing an archer approach, predicted that this man would make arrows from feathers that fell from the birds, which would be able to fly faster than the wings of the birds themselves. These too would be used to kill birds.

The birds all thought that the owl had gone mad, and took no notice of these warning words. However afterward, many of them found out the hard way that her words were true. Then they marveled at her knowledge and decided that she must be the wisest of birds.

But by then it was too late. Now, whenever the birds look up to the owl and ask for her

advice, she no longer
gives it. She just hangs her head and
feels sorry for their earlier stupidity.

Destroy the seed of evil, or it
will grow up to be your ruin.

The Eagle
and the
Hawk

An eagle once sat in the branches of a tree next to a hawk. The lordly bird was sighing and hanging his head in sorrow.

"Whatever is the matter?" asked the hawk. "You seem terribly downcast."

"Oh I am," moaned the eagle. "I've looked everywhere for a suitable mate to keep me company and I simply can't find one."

"Why not take me?" replied the hawk, without hesitating. "I would be a good match for you. In fact, I am much stronger than you."

"Ah, but are you able to live on what you hunt and catch, like I do?" quizzed the eagle.

The hawk shrugged. "Well, I have often caught and carried away a full-grown ostrich in my talons," she insisted.

The eagle was impressed by these words. 'An ostrich,' he thought. 'This hawk must be strong and important indeed.' He didn't need any more thought but accepted the hawk's offer and took her as his mate.

The couple were soon married and held a fine wedding to which all the other birds were invited. Everyone celebrated. Then the eagle and the hawk began the daily business of living together. One day the eagle said to his new wife, "Why don't you fly off and bring me back the ostrich you promised me."

The hawk instantly soared aloft into the air – but when she returned, all she brought back was a straggly mouse, stinking from the length of time it had lain in the fields.

The eagle wrinkled up his beak in disgust. "Is this," he said, "the faithful fulfilment of your promise to me?"

The hawk replied with a smirk, "In order to obtain your royal hand in marriage, there is nothing that I would not have promised."

Do not trust everything people say.

The Eagle and the Crow

A majestic eagle was once perched high up on a lofty rock, from where he could look down on the world beneath him.

Suddenly, something small and white caught his eye, moving far below. At once, he launched himself off the rock and swooped down, seizing a lamb and carrying it off in his talons.

A crow had been standing near the lamb, and this took him quite by surprise. He was full of admiration for the mighty eagle and wished with all his heart that he could be as strong

and swift. So he decided to give it a go. He flew around with a great whir of his wings and settled upon a large ram, intending to carry him off. But his claws became entangled in the ram's fleece and he was not able to get himself free, even though he fluttered with his wings as much as he could.

The shepherd was nearby and saw what had happened. He at once ran over and seized the crow.

Once he had cut him free from the ram's wool, he clipped his wings so he could no longer fly. That evening he took him home and gave him to his children as a pet.

The children were delighted and quizzed their father, saying, "Wherever did you find it? And what sort of a bird is it?"

He replied, "To my knowledge it is a crow, but it would like you to think it is an eagle."

If you pretend to be something you are not, prepare to be found out.

The Crow and the Doves

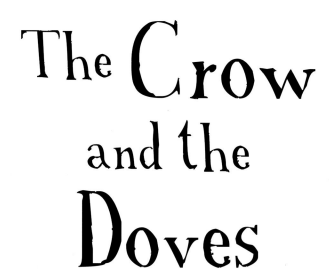

Once there was a crow who saw that some doves living in a warm, safe birdhouse were provided with food by their owner. The crow wished to share in this easy life and tried to disguise himself as a dove by painting himself white.

The unwitting doves didn't notice and let him into their house.

The crafty crow was careful to be silent, so he wouldn't give himself away by letting the gentle-voiced doves hear his harsh cry. However, the longer he spent with them the more relaxed he became. One day he forgot himself and began to chatter. Horrified, the doves kicked him out at once, pecking him hard.

So the crow returned to his own kind. But because he was white, his friends failed to recognize

him. They too turned him away.

So in trying to win favor with two sets of birds, he ended up gaining neither.

If you try to be all things to all people, you may well please no one — not even yourself.